play guitar with...

led zeppelin
the blues

play guitar with...

led zeppelin
the blues

Wise Publications
part of The Music Sales Group
London / New York / Paris / Sydney / Copenhagen / Berlin / Madrid / Tokyo

Published by
Wise Publications
14-15 Berners Street, London W1T 3LJ, UK

Exclusive Distributors:
Music Sales Limited
Distribution Centre, Newmarket Road,
Bury St Edmunds, Suffolk IP33 3YB, UK
Music Sales Pty Limited
120 Rothschild Avenue,
Rosebery, NSW 2018, Australia

Order No. AM985380
ISBN 1-84609-507-7
This book © Copyright 2006 Wise Publications,
a division of Music Sales Limited.

Compiled by Nick Crispin
Music arranged by Arthur Dick
Music processed by Paul Ewers Music Design
Cover designed by Fresh Lemon
Cover photograph courtesy of Michael Putland / Retna
Printed in the EU

CD recorded, mixed and mastered by Jonas Persson & John Rose
All guitars by Arthur Dick
Organ & Electric Piano by Paul Honey
Harmonica by Stuart Constable
Bass by Paul Townsend
Drums by Chris Baron

Your Guarantee of Quality
As publishers, we strive to produce
every book to the highest commercial standards.
The music has been freshly engraved and the book has
been carefully designed to minimise awkward page turns
and to make playing from it a real pleasure.
Particular care has been given to specifying acid-free,
neutral-sized paper made from pulps which have not been
elemental chlorine bleached. This pulp is from farmed
sustainable forests and was produced with
special regard for the environment.
Throughout, the printing and binding have been planned
to ensure a sturdy, attractive publication which
should give years of enjoyment.
If your copy fails to meet our high standards,
please inform us and we will gladly replace it.

www.musicsales.com

guitar tablature explained

guitar music can be notated in three different ways: on a musical stave, in tablature, and in rhythm slashes

RHYTHM SLASHES: are written above the stave. Strum chords in the rhythm indicated. Round noteheads indicate single notes.

THE MUSICAL STAVE: shows pitches and rhythms and is divided by lines into bars. Pitches are named after the first seven letters of the alphabet.

TABLATURE: graphically represents the guitar fingerboard. Each horizontal line represents a string, and each number represents a fret.

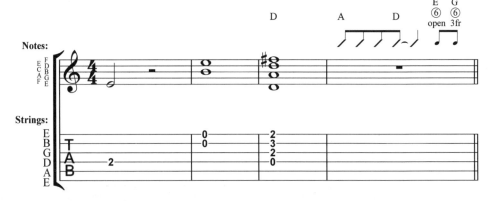

definitions for special guitar notation

SEMI-TONE BEND: Strike the note and bend up a semi-tone (½ step).

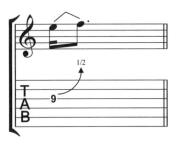

WHOLE-TONE BEND: Strike the note and bend up a whole-tone (full step).

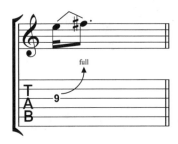

GRACE NOTE BEND: Strike the note and bend as indicated. Play the first note as quickly as possible.

QUARTER-TONE BEND: Strike the note and bend up a ¼ step

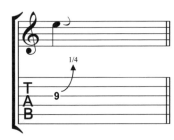

BEND & RELEASE: Strike the note and bend up as indicated, then release back to the original note.

COMPOUND BEND & RELEASE: Strike the note and bend up and down in the rhythm indicated.

PRE-BEND: Bend the note as indicated, then strike it.

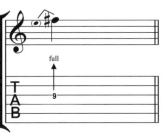

PRE-BEND & RELEASE: Bend the note as indicated. Strike it and release the note back to the original pitch.

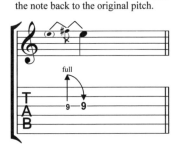

HAMMER-ON: Strike the first note with one finger, then sound the second note (on the same string) with another finger by fretting it without picking.

PULL-OFF: Place both fingers on the note to be sounded, strike the first note and without picking, pull the finger off to sound the second note.

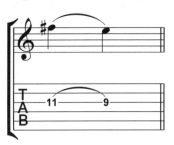

LEGATO SLIDE (GLISS): Strike the first note and then slide the same fret-hand finger up or down to the second note. The second note is not struck.

MUFFLED STRINGS: A percussive sound is produced by laying the first hand across the string(s) without depressing, and striking them with the pick hand.

NATURAL HARMONIC: Strike the note while the fret-hand lightly touches the string directly over the fret indicated.

PICK SCRAPE: The edge of the pick is rubbed down (or up) the string, producing a scratchy sound.

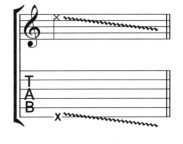

PALM MUTING: The note is partially muted by the pick hand lightly touching the string(s) just before the bridge.

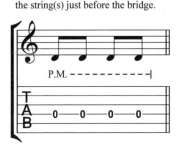

SHIFT SLIDE (GLISS & RESTRIKE) Same as legato slide, except the second note is struck.

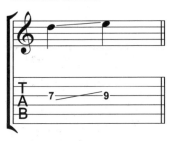

6

SLAP HARMONIC: The note is fretted normally and a harmonic is produced by 'slapping' or tapping the fret indicated in brackets (which will be twelve frets higher than the fretted note.)

TAPPING: Hammer ('tap') the fret indicated with the pick-hand index or middle finger and pull-off to the note fretted by the fret hand.

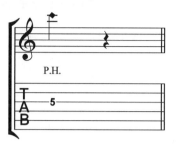

PINCH HARMONIC: The note is fretted normally and a harmonic is produced by adding the edge of the thumb or the tip of the index finger of the pick hand to the normal pick attack.

HARP HARMONIC: The note is fretted normally and a harmonic is produced by gently resting the pick hand's index finger directly above the indicated fret (in brackets) while plucking the appropriate string.

TRILL: Very rapidly alternate between the notes indicated by continuously hammering-on and pulling-off.

RAKE: Drag the pick across the strings with a single motion.

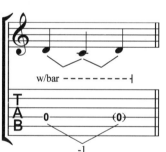

TREMOLO PICKING: The note is picked as rapidly and continously as possible.

ARPEGGIATE: Play the notes of the chord indicated by quickly rolling them from bottom to top.

SWEEP PICKING: Rhythmic downstroke and/or upstroke motion across the strings.

VIBRATO DIVE BAR AND RETURN: The pitch of the note or chord is dropped a specific number of steps (in rhythm) then returned to the original pitch.

VIBRATO BAR SCOOP: Depress the bar just before striking the note, then quickly release the bar.

VIBRATO BAR DIP: Strike the note and then immediately drop a specific number of steps, then release back to the original pitch.

additional musical definitions

 (accent) Accentuate note (play it louder)

D.S. al Coda — Go back to the sign (𝄋), then play until the bar marked ***To Coda*** ⊕ then skip to the section marked ⊕ ***Coda***

(accent) Accentuate note with greater intensity

D.C. al Fine — Go back to the beginning of the song and play until the bar marked ***Fine.***

 (staccato) Shorten time value of note

tacet — Instrument is silent (drops out).

 Downstroke

∨ Upstroke

 Repeat bars between signs

NOTE: Tablature numbers in brackets mean:
1. The note is sustained, but a new articulation (such as hammer-on or slide) begins
2. A note may be fretted but not necessarily played.

When a repeat section has different endings, play the first ending only the first time and the second ending only the second time.

7

babe, I'm gonna leave you

Words & Music by Anne Bredon
Arranged by Jimmy Page & Robert Plant

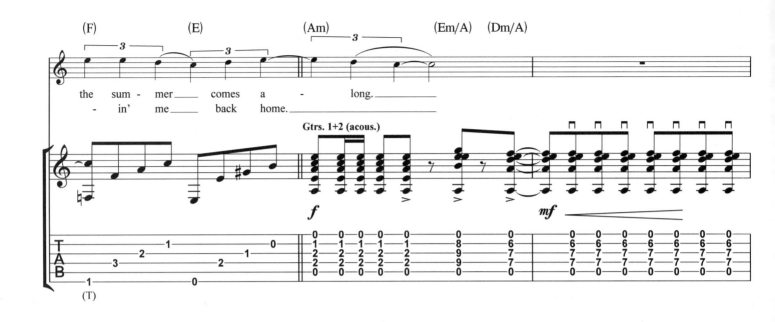

the sum - mer____ comes a - long.____
- in' me____ back home.____

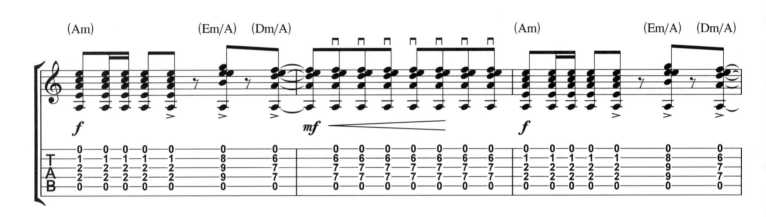

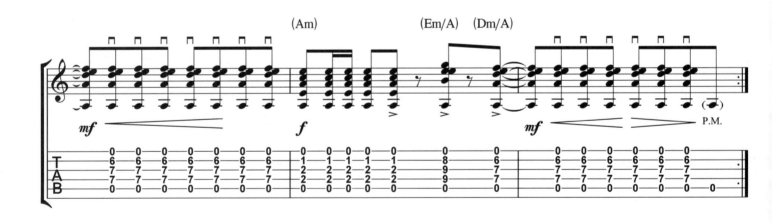

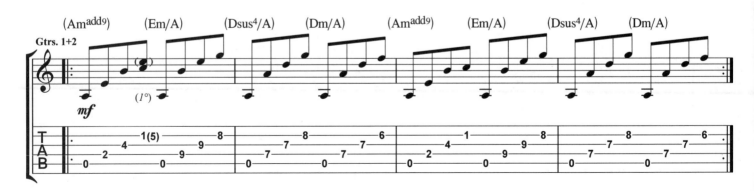

Chorus

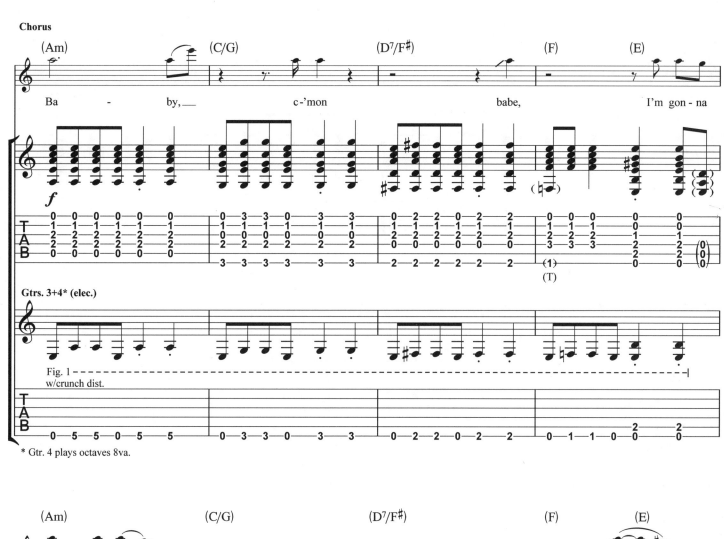

* Gtr. 4 plays octaves 8va.

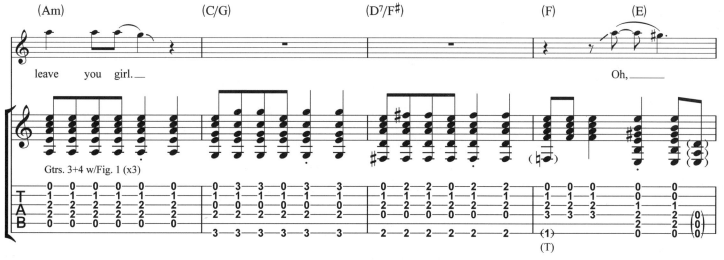

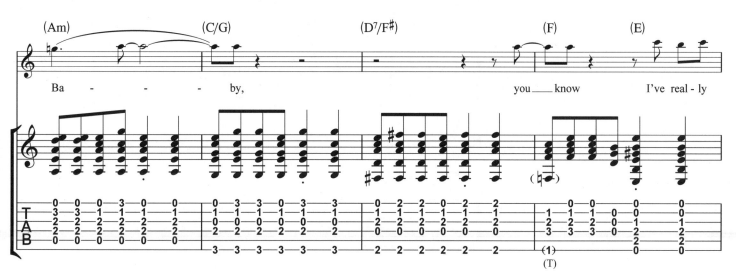

11

Bridge

15

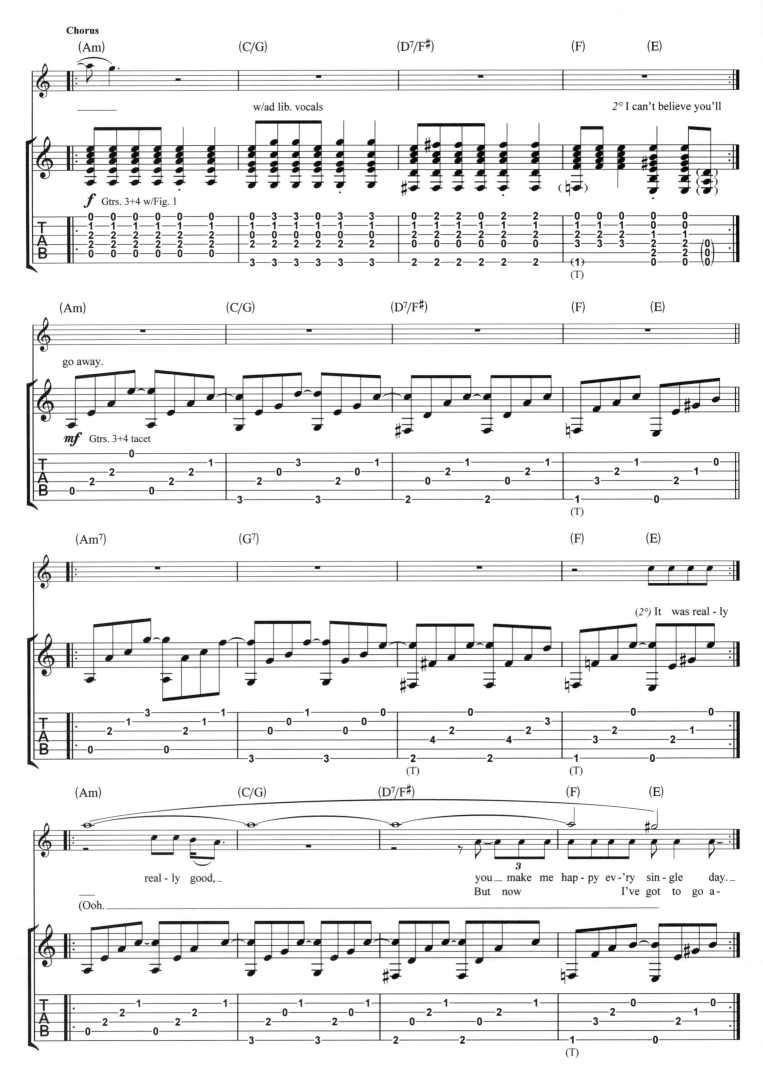

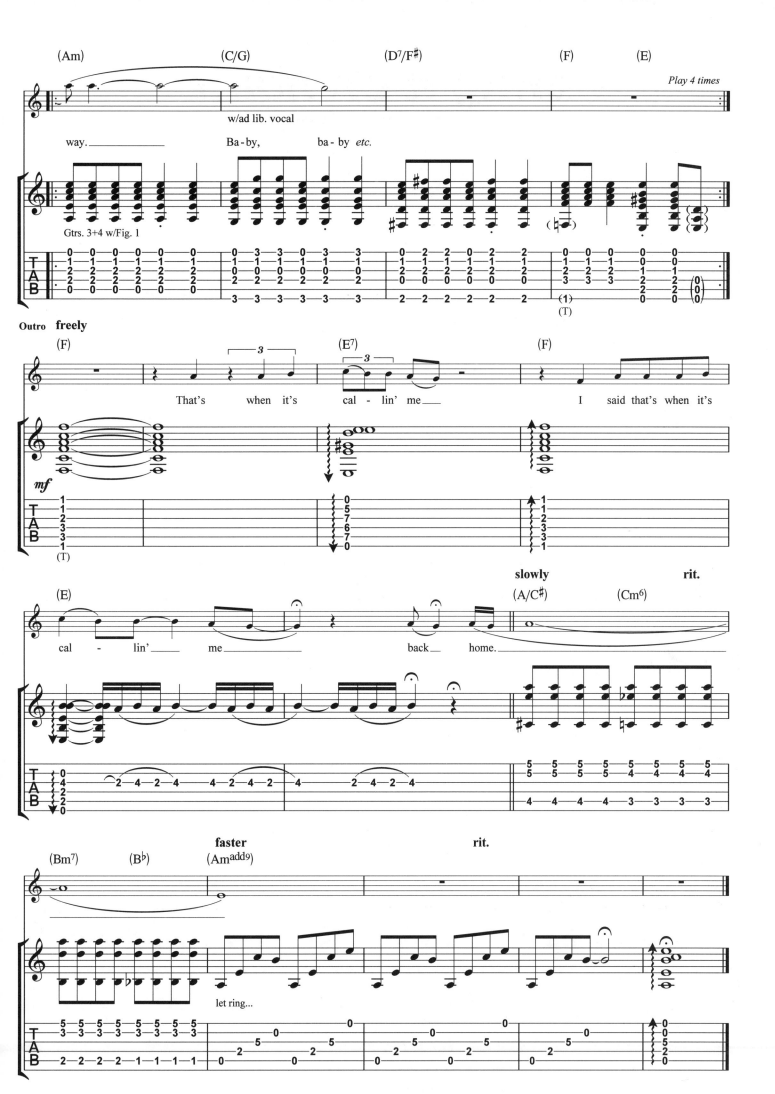

bring it on home

Words & Music by Willie Dixon

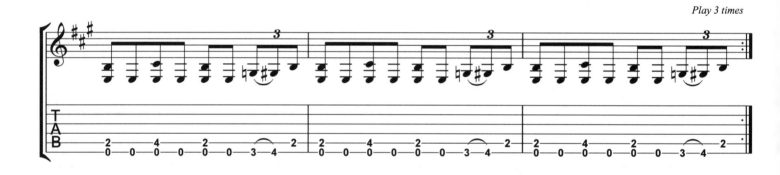

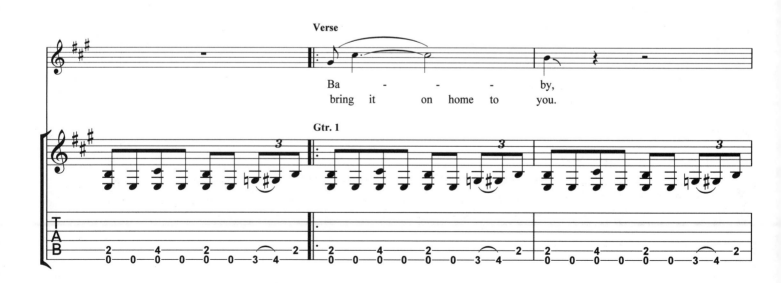

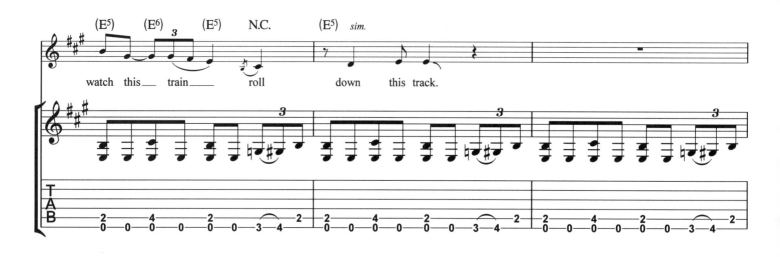

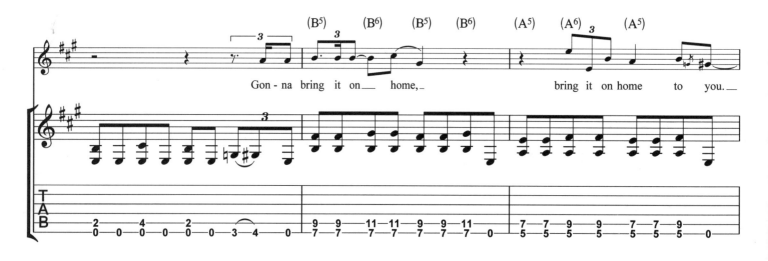

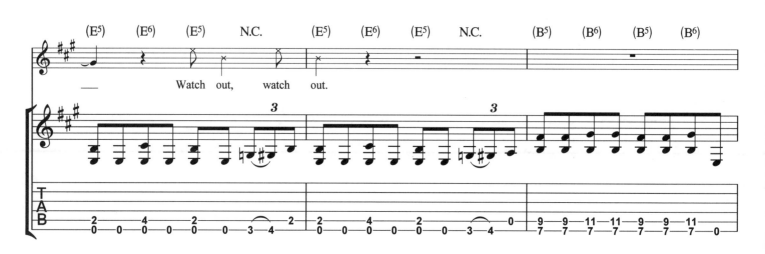

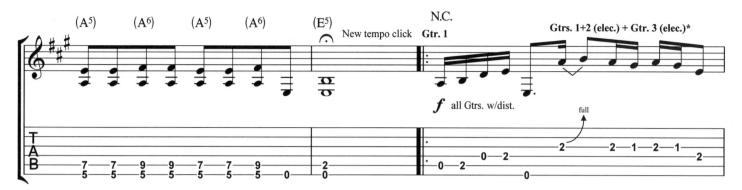

Play Gtr. 1 part
* Gtr. 3 plays 8va for 4 bars, then harmony (in 6ths) for 4 bars.

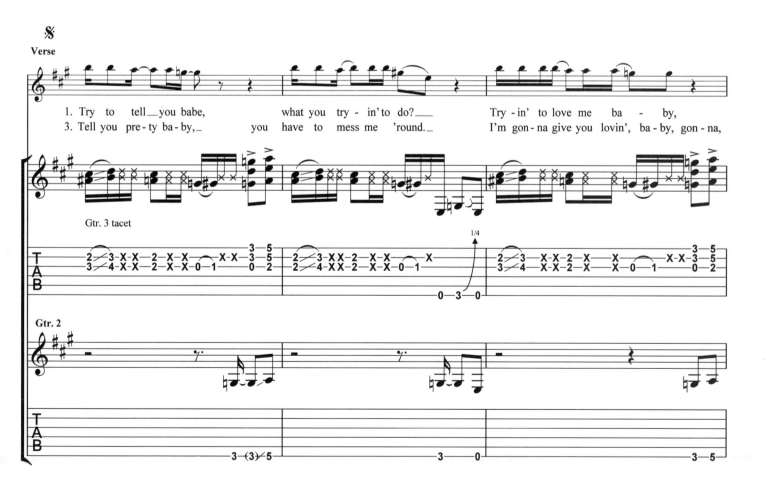

1. Try to tell you babe,   what you try - in' to do?   Try - in' to love me ba - by,
3. Tell you pre - ty ba - by,   you have to mess me 'round.   I'm gon - na give you lovin', ba - by, gon - na,

Gtr. 3 tacet

Gtr. 2

love some oth-er man too,_ well bring it on home. Bring it on home.
move you out_ of town.   Bring it on home.   Bring it on home.

Verse

2. Went a lit-tle walk down town, messed and got__ back__ late.__
4. Sweet-est lit-tle ba-by,   Dad-dy ev-er____ saw.

Found a note___ there   wait - ing,   it said___   "Dad - dy, I___   just can't   wait!"___   Bring   it   on
I'm   gon - na___ give   you___ lov - in' ba - by,   I'm gon - na___   give   you   more.___   Bring   it   on

home.   Bring   it   on   home._____   Bring   it   on
home.   Bring   it   on   home._____   Bring   it   on

home._____
home._____

Bring it back   home_____   to me ba - - - - by._____
Bring it back   home._____   Al - - - right!

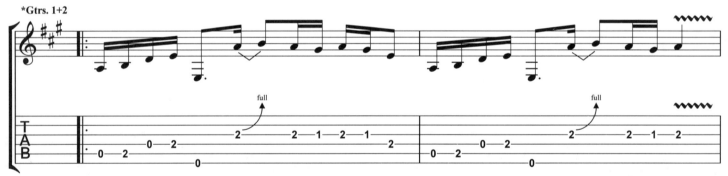

*Gtrs. 1+2

* Gtr. 3 plays 8va for 4 bars, then harmony (in 6ths) for 4 bars.

To Coda ⊕   *D.S. al Coda*

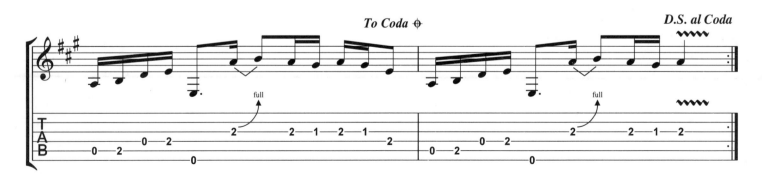

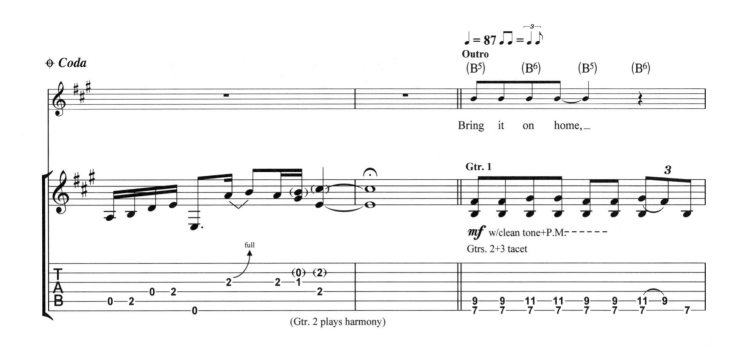

Bring it on home,—

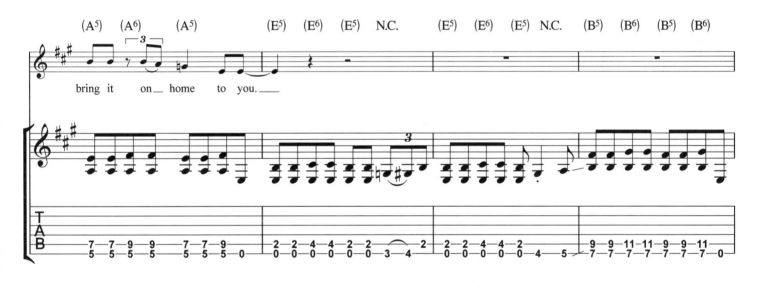

bring it on— home to you.——

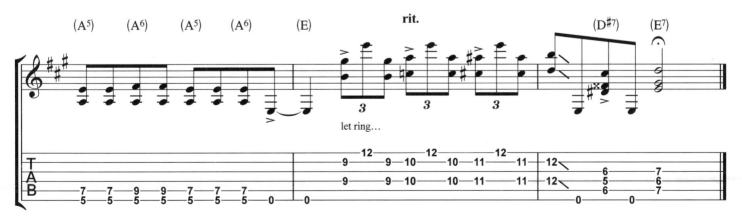

let ring…

I can't quit you baby

Words & Music by Willie Dixon

Said you messed up my hap-py home,

made me mis-treat my on-ly child. Yes it did babe.

Oh. Said you know I love you ba - by,

my love for you, I could nev - er hide.

Oh, you know I love you babe,

my love for you I could nev - er hide.

Ah, when I feel you near me lit - tle girl

I know you are my one des - ire. Oh!

28

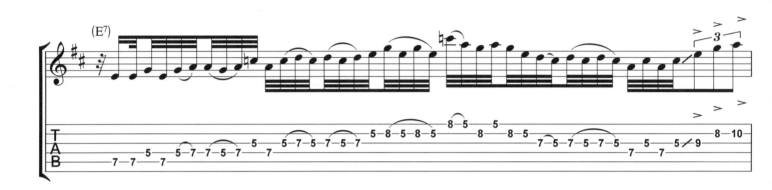

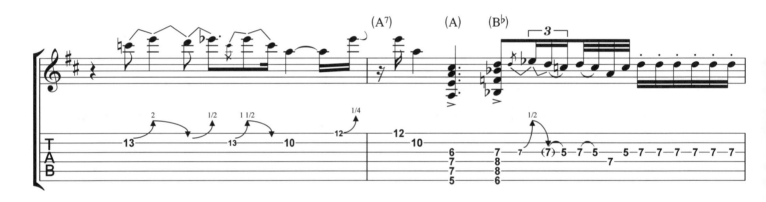

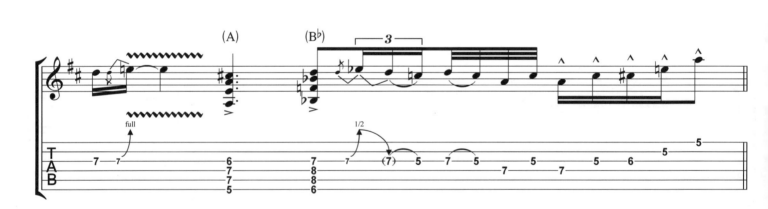

Freely

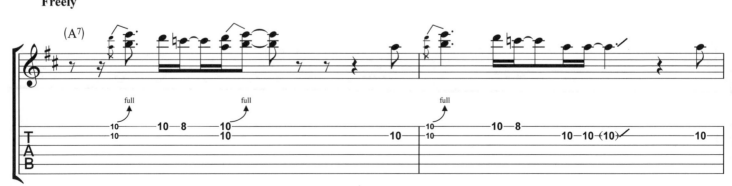

when you here me moan-in' and groan-in' babe,   you know it hurts me deep down in-

- side.   Oh! ___

When you hear me hol-ler ba - by,   don't ___ know your my one ___ de - sire. ___

(approx. pitch)

Yes you   are.   oh!

the lemon song

Words & Music by Jimmy Page, Robert Plant, John Paul Jones, John Bonham & Chester Burnett

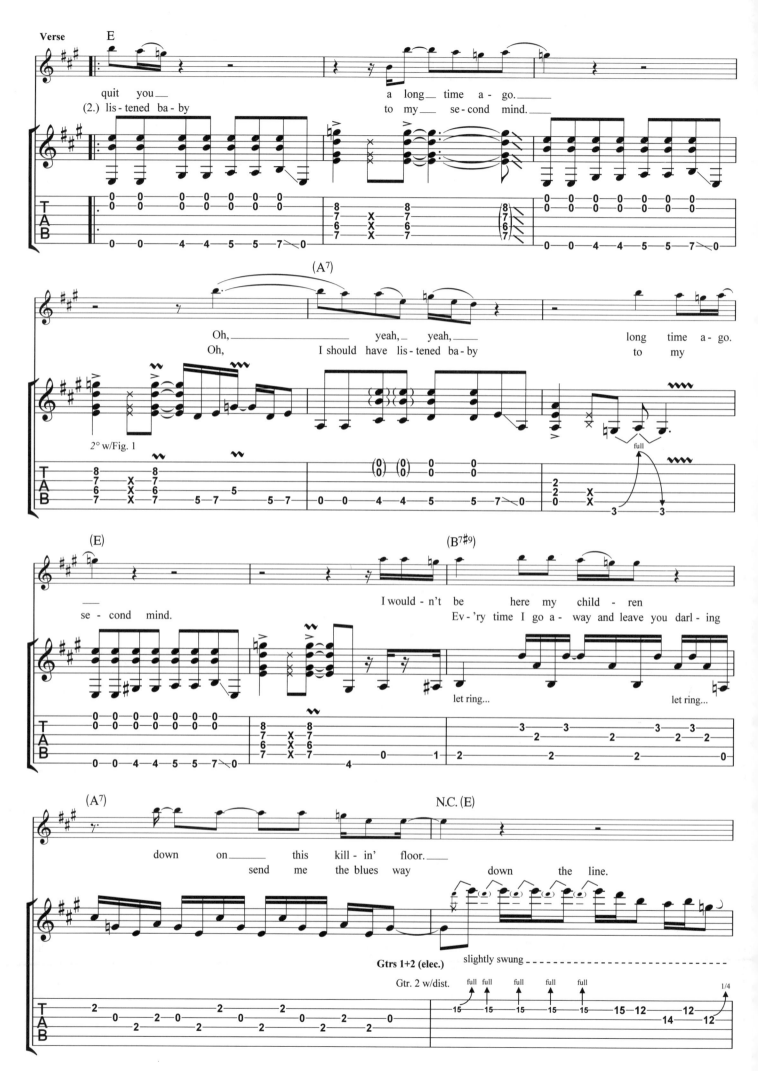

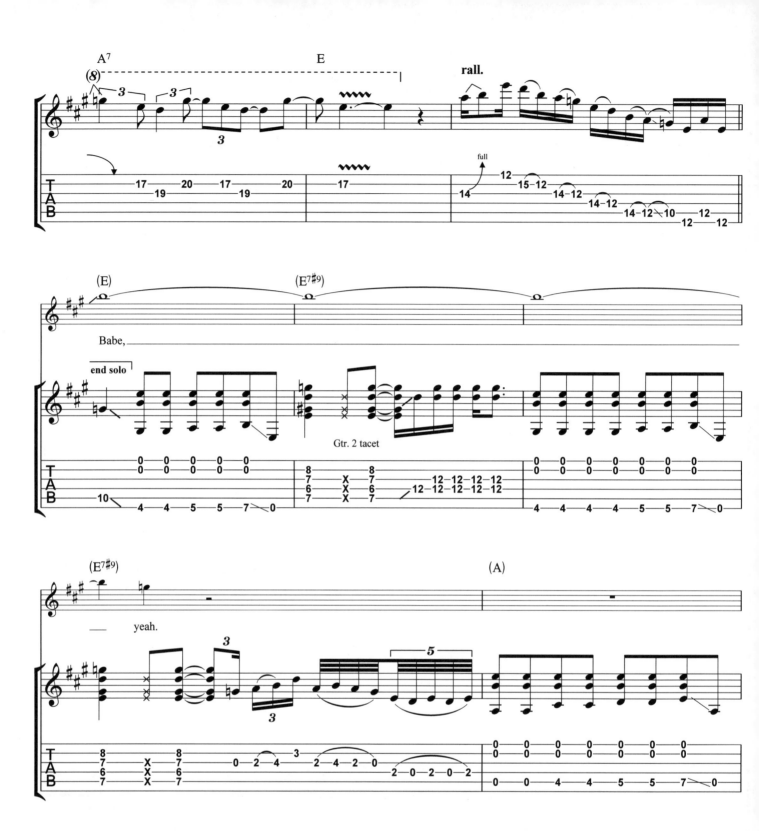

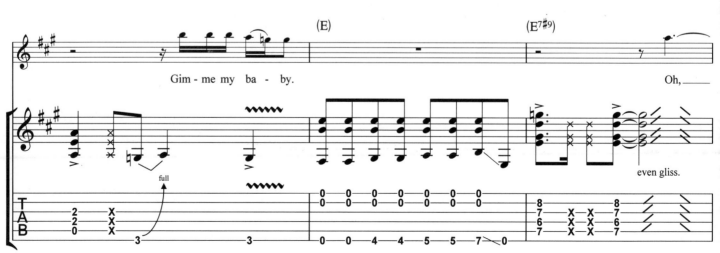

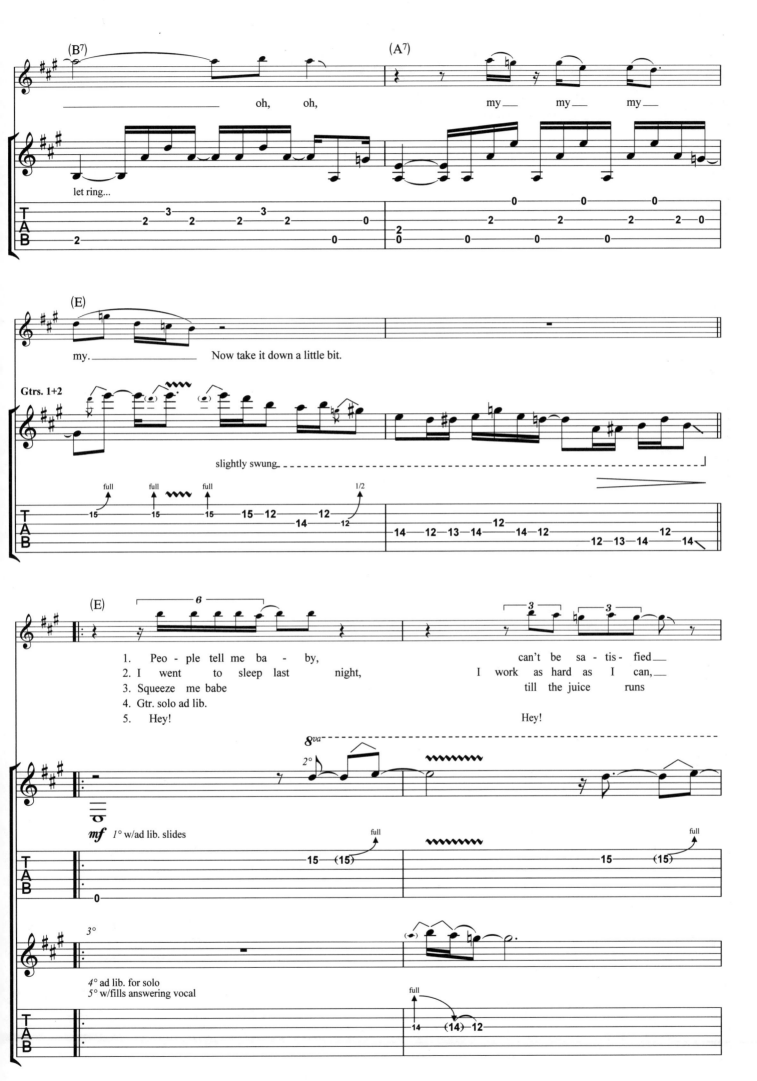

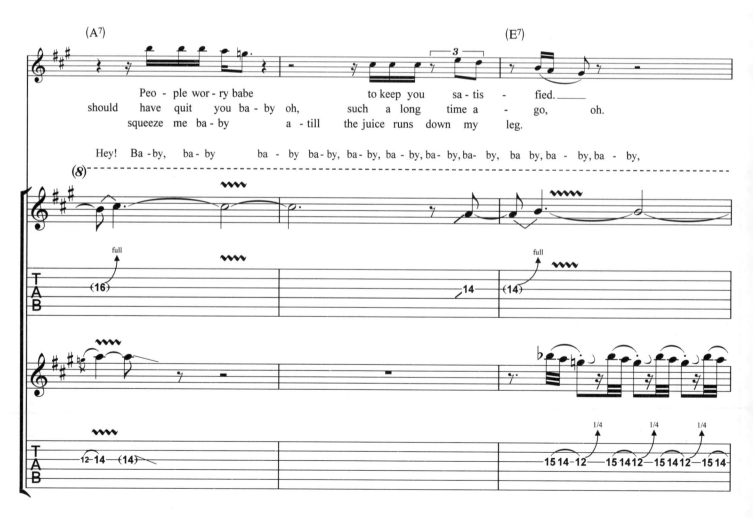

Ah,   let me tell you babe   ah,_____ you ain't no - thin' but a_____ two bit__ no good__
I would - n't be here with all my trou - bles,   down on this   kill - in'
The way you squeeze my le - mon, I   I'm gon - na fall right out

Hey!   Hey!   Hey!   Hey!   Hey!   Hey!

_____ jive._____
floor._____
of   bed,   bed,   bed,   bed._____

cont. w/ad lib. solo

* Bend string with right hand behind the nut while trilling with left!

41

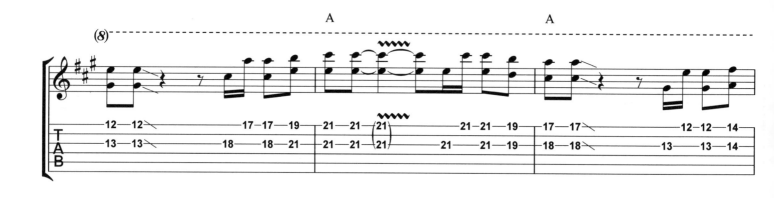

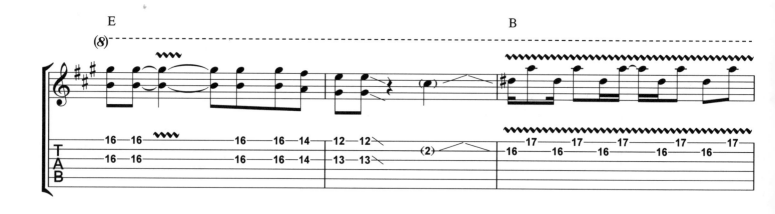

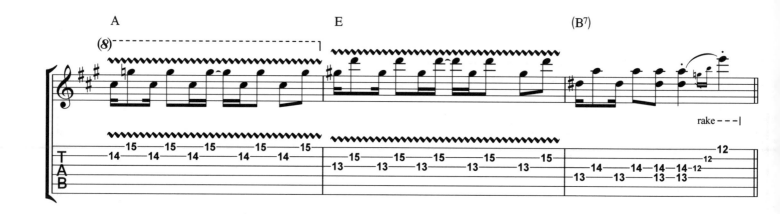

we're gonna groove

Words & Music by Ben E. King & James Bethea

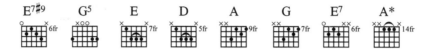

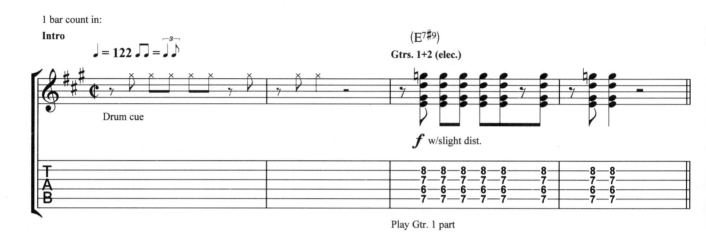

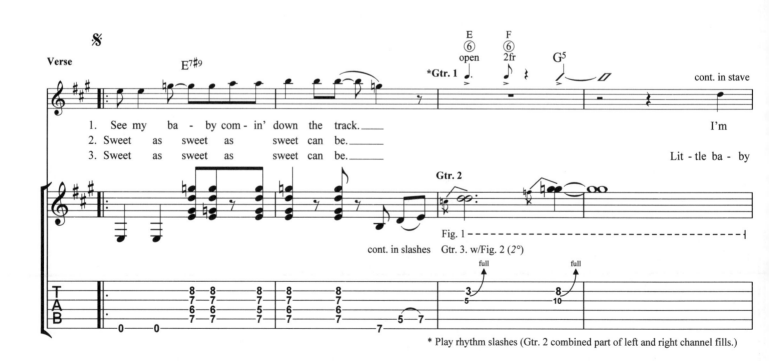

* Play rhythm slashes (Gtr. 2 combined part of left and right channel fills.)

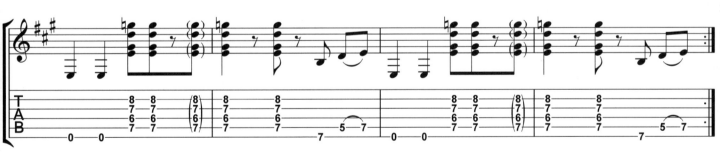
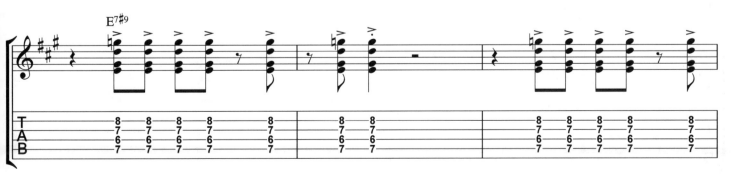

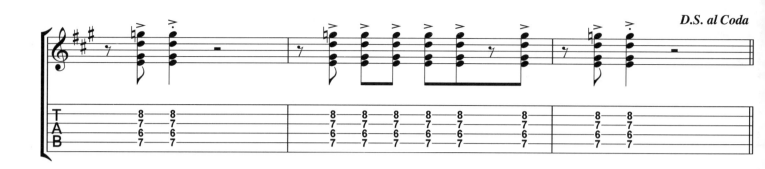

Coda

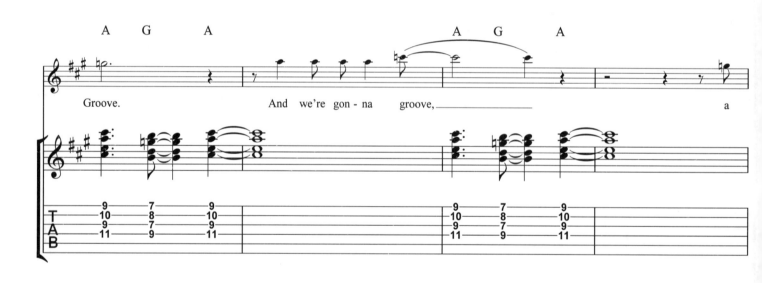

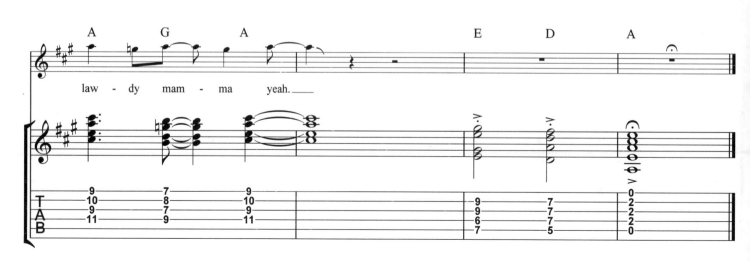

you shook me

Words & Music by Willie Dixon & J.B. Lenoir

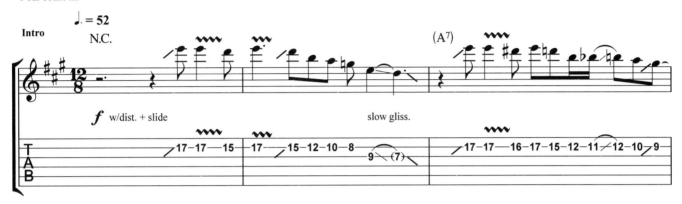

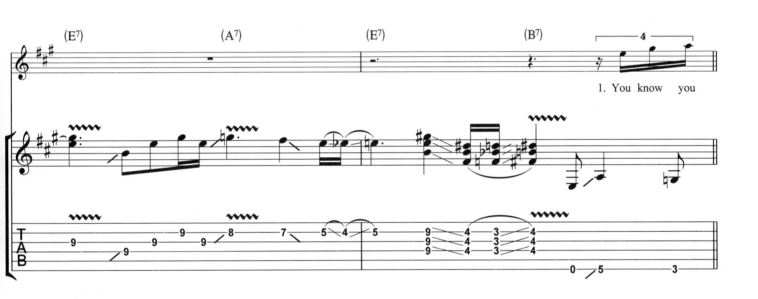

buy a dia-mond ring___ hey!

Solo

(1° Organ, 2° Blues Harp)

mf w/variable P.M.
2° sim. ad lib.

let ring... swing

1.

let ring...

let ring...

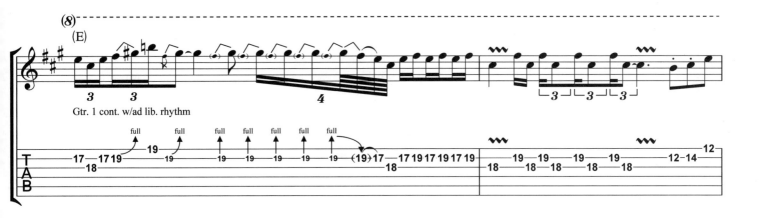

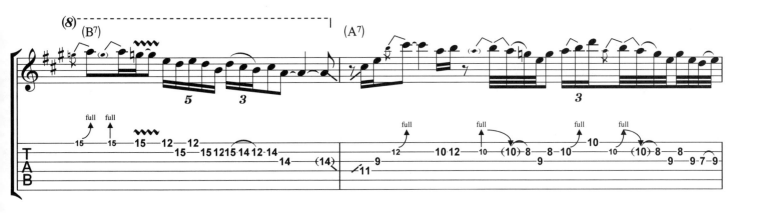

10/07(63667)

play guitar with...

...the legends of rock - over 80 great book & CD titles to collect!

AC/DC
Includes:
back in black
highway to hell
whole lotta rosie
Order No. AM955900

the beatles
Includes:
day tripper
get back
yesterday
Order No. NO90665

the beatles Book 2
Includes:
eight days a week
please please me
ticket to ride
Order No. NO90667

the beatles Book 3
Includes:
here comes the sun
revolution
while my guitar gently weeps
Order No. NO90689

chuck berry
Includes:
round and around
johnny b. goode
no particular place to go
Order No. AM943789

black sabbath
Includes:
iron man
paranoid
war pigs
Order No. AM955911

blur
Includes:
country house
girls and boys
parklife
Order No. AM935320

bon jovi
the early years
Includes:
livin' on a prayer
wanted dead or alive
you give love a bad name
Order No. AM971256

eric clapton
Includes:
layla
sunshine of your love
tears in heaven
Order No. AM950862

phil collins
Includes:
another day in paradise
don't lose my number
one more night
Order No. AM928147

the corrs
Includes:
forgiven, not forgotten
so young
what can i do
Order No. AM960971

the cranberries
Includes:
dollywood
ridiculous thoughts
zombie
Order No. AM941699

dire straits
Includes:
money for nothing
romeo and juliet
sultans of swing
Order No. DG70735

free
Includes:
all right now
fire and water
wishing well
Order No. AM960960

david gilmour
Includes:
learning to fly
on the turning away
take it back
Order No. AM954602

buddy holly
Includes:
rave on
words of love
peggy sue
Order No. AM943734

john lee hooker
Includes:
boom boom
the healer
i'm in the mood
Order No. AM951885

b. b. king
Includes:
every day i have the blues
rock me baby
the thrill is gone
Order No. AM951874

the kinks
Includes:
all day and all of the night
waterloo sunset
you really got me
Order No. AM951863

kula shaker
Includes:
govinda
hey dude
hush
Order No. AM943767

john lennon
Includes:
cold turkey
happy xmas (war is over)
woman
Order No. AM943756

bob marley
Includes:
i shot the sheriff
jamming
no woman, no cry
Order No. AM937739

metallica
Includes:
enter sandman
fade to black
the unforgiven
Order No. AM92559

metallica Book 2
Includes:
creeping death
seek and destroy
whiskey in the jar
Order No. AM955977

alanis morissette
Includes:
hand in my pocket
ironic
you oughta know
Order No. AM943723

oasis
Includes:
cigarettes & alcohol
morning glory
supersonic
Order No. AM935330

ocean colour scene
Includes:
the circle
the day we caught the train
the riverboat song
Order No. AM943712

elvis presley
Includes:
all shook up
blue suede shoes
hound dog
Order No. AM937090

pulp
Includes:
common people
disco 2000
sorted for e's & wizz
Order No. AM938124

the rolling stones
Includes:
brown sugar
(i can't get no) satisfaction
jumpin' jack flash
Order No. AM90247

stereophonics
Includes:
just looking
pick a part that's new
the bartender & the thief
Order No. AM960950

sting
Includes:
an englishman in new york
fields of gold
if you love somebody
set them free
Order No. AM928092

the stone roses
Includes:
i am the resurrection
i wanna be adored
ten storey love song
Order No. AM943701

the stone roses Book 2
Includes:
fool's gold
love spreads
one love
Order No. AM955890

suede
Includes:
animal nitrate
electricity
we are the pigs
Order No. AM955955

paul weller
Includes:
the changingman
out of the sinking
wild wood
Order No. AM937827

the who
Includes:
i can see for miles
pinball wizard
substitute
Order No. AM955867

the 60's
Includes:
all along the watchtower
(jimi hendrix)
born to be wild (steppenwolf)
not fade away (the rolling stones)
Order No. AM957748

the 70's
Includes:
all right now (free)
hotel california (the eagles)
live and let die (wings)
Order No. AM957759

the 80's
Includes:
addicted to love (robert palmer)
need you tonight (inxs)
where the streets have no
name (u2)
Order No. AM957760

the 90's
Includes:
everything must go
(manic street preachers)
love is the law (the seahorses)
wonderwall (oasis)
Order No. AM957770

blues legends
Includes:
crossroads blues (cream)
couldn't stand the weather
(stevie ray vaughan)
killing floor (jimi hendrix)
Order No. AM958507

classic tracks
Includes:
every breath you take (the police)
hey joe (jimi hendrix)
ziggy stardust (david bowie)
Order No. AM961004

pop anthems
Includes:
angels (robbie williams)
road rage (catatonia)
what can i do (the corrs)
Order No. AM960982

the metal album
Includes:
fade to black (metallica)
live and let die (guns n' roses)
love bites (def leppard)
Order No. AM954426

the gold book
Includes:
johnny b. goode (chuck berry)
layla (eric clapton)
sultans of swing (dire straits)
Order No. AM951907

the platinum book
Includes:
a design for life (manic street
preachers)
cigarettes & alcohol (oasis)
the riverboat song
(ocean colour scene)
Order No. AM951918

...and many more!

CD track listing

1 *tuning notes*

Full instrumental performances (with guitar)...

2 *babe, I'm gonna leave you*
(Bredon/Page/Plant) Warner/Chappell Music Limited/
Universal Music Limited

3 *bring it on home*
(Dixon) Bug Music Limited.

4 *I can't quit you baby*
(Dixon) Bug Music Limited.

5 *the lemon song*
(Page/Plant/Jones/Bonham/Burnett)
Jewel Music Publishing Company Limited.

6 *we're gonna groove*
(King/Bethea) Milky Way Publishing Company Incorporated, USA/
Twangy Music Limited.

7 *you shook me*
(Dixon/Lenoir) Jewel Music Publishing Company Limited/
Bug Music Limited.

Backing tracks only (without guitar)...

8 *babe, I'm gonna leave you*
9 *bring it on home*
10 *I can't quit you baby*
11 *the lemon song*
12 *we're gonna groove*
13 *you shook me*

> To remove your CD from the plastic sleeve,
> lift the small lip to break the perforations.
> Replace the disc after use for convenient storage.